Our Family
A Personal Record

THIS IS A CARLTON BOOK

Text and design copyright © 1997 Carlton Books Limited

This edition published by Strathearn Books Limited
in association with Carlton Books Limited 1997
20 St Anne's Court, Wardour Street, London W1V 3AW

A CIP catalogue for this book is available from the British Library

ISBN 1.85868.374.2

Project Editor: Sarah Larter
Art Editor: Zoë Maggs
Designer: Kaye Lyall
Picture research: Rachel Leach
Production: Alexia Rencricca

Printed in Italy

OUR FAMILY HISTORY

A Personal Record

Karen and Martin Fido

STRATHEARN BOOKS LIMITED
Toronto, Canada

For our dearest cousin,
Margaret Townsend Warren

Contents

Introduction

Starting to trace your family history

In our country we live in a society whose people live increasingly far from their places of origin. Except for those of pure Native-American descent, our ancestors all came from some place else. Many of us live very far from where we were born, and our parents and their parents before them may have done the same. A sense of continuity in family life becomes increasingly difficult to sustain in the highly mobile world we live in today. And we cannot forget the inherent curiosity in all of us that compels us to ask, "Where did I spring from and what makes me what I am today?"

The long-standing controversy surrounding heredity *vs* environment is likely to continue unabated, but scientists continue to discover ways in which we can be shown to be products of our heredity. Studies of twins separated at birth prove beyond a doubt that inherited genes play a

huge part in determining our true natures. In the fascinating case of the Argyll family of Great Britain, even a characteristic handwriting has been handed down from one ancestor to another. Those who were adopted at birth search with great dedication for their biological family, deeming this to be essential if they are to know who they are.

Perhaps the best reason of all for starting a family tree is that genealogy is fun. Imagine you have just bought an antique desk. How much more you would cherish it if you knew who had owned it and when and where! Just think of learning that a great piece of literature was written by a famous author seated at your very own desk! The same thrill can await you when you discover the life histories of some particularly interesting ancestors. It may be possible to learn that a great-great-grandmother crossed the country in a covered wagon and she documented that journey. To read her observations of the hardships she endured is to see her character revealed. Old photographs and letters provide a real glimpse into the lives of family members who have gone before us. A moving example of this lies in a recently discovered letter written during the Civil War.

It was found in the possession of a distant family member. A young soldier writes to his mother to inform her of the circumstances of his twin brother's death in battle. A photograph of the boys together in uniform was found in yet another relative's family album.

Of course an ancestor need not have been a war hero. Every family had its horse thief or can boast of a black sheep of some sort somewhere in their lineage. They are sometimes the most intriguing predecessors of all. If we trace back far enough, we will find out ancestors came from all walks of life. Snobbery has no place in genealogy. Although almost everyone has royal blood, the difficulty lies in trying to trace it. All genealogists are aware that if we could follow out ancestry back to Genesis we would realize how truly we are all part of one family – the family of mankind. Some lines of descent can be traced back further than others since for various reasons people adopted surnames at different times in history. But we must understand that one family is no older than any other.

As you might expect, the earliest genealogies are those of royal and sacred families. In Japan, royal and noble lineage has been recorded through the male line since the beginning of written records – a very long time indeed. There are Chinese people alive today who can trace their descent back through seventy six generations to the great sage Confucius himself who was born in 51 BCE, and who was a direct descendant of the Dukes of Sung who lived during the period 1766–1122 BCE. In Europe, due to the recording of numerous royal marriages, a surprising number of people are able to find royal descent.

Where do you start? Genealogy has been described as a cross between a good detective story and a jigsaw puzzle. The purpose of this book is to serve as a guide through the adventure of compiling a family history. The importance of good record keeping is stressed. What you learn must be preserved for future generations. Once you begin your search, you will perhaps meet relatives you never knew existed, or travel to places unknown to you. Many exciting experiences await you, so let us begin!

Genealogy and family history

As a family historian you must understand the difference between family history and genealogy. Genealogy studies pedigree, and establishes lines of descent. Genealogists' research goals are the names and dates proving and documenting genetic relationships. Although you will do some of this work, your goals as a family historian are rather different.

This book begins with you and your immediate family. You will record some genealogical information about each entry, but you will also give details of personal lives. This takes you beyond the concerns of the genealogist, who may be only incidentally interested in many fascinating family facts.

Genealogy gives the bare bones of people's descent and relationships; it is the interesting task of the family historian to put flesh on them. Once we know who Grandfather Clark's parents were, where and when he was born and died, who he married, and when and where each of his children was born, we have completed the genealogist's main work; indeed, these basic facts must be established before we can do the family historian's work of giving some idea of what Grandfather Clark was really like.

Yet genealogical data give many clues to an ancestor's life. Did he live through a war or some social upheaval? Did he die far from his birthplace? If so, why? The family historian uses genealogical clues to find answers. Think of your own life. It would be difficult for future generations to learn about you without some understanding of the times and places in which you have lived.

Compiling your family history is a deeply rewarding task. Future generations will learn about you and yours. They will enjoy your discoveries about more remote relatives. This book may prove more than a cherished heirloom: it could become the starting point for other people's research. So make your record as accurate and fully documented as possible.

Getting organized

What do you need before you start? First, a looseleaf notebook with paper. Make it your workbook. Write everything down in pencil in it before filling in this album.

Organizing your workbook helps avoid error. For example, the same first names often recur in families, sometimes within the same generation. Different people with the same names are easily confused. Avoid this by the simple system called 'coding'. If you turn to pages 60–67 you will see a section called 'Our Family Tree' with spaces to record six generations of your and your spouse's families. Now, in your workbook, designate one page to each person you are entering in the album. You can add more looseleaf sheets later as you need them. Each person should be identified by a three figure code telling at a glance their generation, and whether they are of your or your spouse's family, and giving them a personal number within their generation.

Sounds complicated, but it isn't really. Take yourself to begin with. You and your spouse are the first generation you are recording, so the first figure of your code is the number 1. And 1 will also be the first figure for your brothers and sisters and your brothers-in-law and sisters-in-law, and your first cousins.

The next generation you trace back to – that of your parents and uncles and aunts – will carry the first code number 2. Your four grandparents, and your spouse's, and all your spouse's and your great-aunts and great-uncles constitute the generation which starts its coding with the figure 3. Great-greats will start with a 4. That's easy enough, isn't it?

The next code entry is easier still. You don't need documents to know whether you are husband or wife in your marriage. And the second entry in the code is either an H or a W to sort out the two family lines leading down to your children. You and your partner, then, as the first-entered generation 'Mr and Mrs' are coded 1H and 1W. Husband's siblings and cousins are 1H and wife's are 1W. The husband's parents, aunts and uncles start coding 2H: the wife's are 2W. Grandparents and great-aunts and great- uncles are 3W and 3H. And so on.

Finally every person entered has a per-

sonal number so that you know just which person in each generation is being described. Let's take you and your spouse first. You'll number yourselves 1, the first person on each side of the H and W division. So husband is fully coded 1H1; and wife is 1W1. The husband's first sibling will become 1H2; the wife's 1W2. And so it goes through to your cousins. You might have first cousins who became 1W4 and 1W5; their parents, the wife's aunt and uncle might be 2W3 and 2W4 (the wife's parents being 2W1 and 2W2).

You may find it helpful to pencil these code numbers lightly beside the spaces for names in the album. Then with a small number in the album and the same number heading a page in your workbook, you will know which data refer to which person and avoid confusion until your entry is complete and the pencil mark can be erased.

So make up your notebook pages with the code number at the top above the person's name and personal data, and arrange the pages in code numerical order with dividers, if you like, separating the generations.

You will see that you don't have codes

for your children and grandchildren. You don't need them. You know who they are and won't get them mixed up! Just make pages for each of them to put at the beginning or end of the notebook.

You will also need somewhere to file miscellaneous documents. These may be originals or copies of birth, marriage or death certificates. They may be letters or diaries, or various things you have acquired. 'Family Sources' on page 94 gives a fuller list of what you might be storing.

Your miscellaneous file can be a large desk drawer, a file cabinet or even a big box. Material filed in it should be organized with the same coding system as your notebook, and kept in numerical code order. Remember that even if information obtained about a family member cannot be used now, it may prove invaluable some day. Future generations may bless you for preserving something that seemed useless. Photographs should have permanent identifying information recorded on their backs if it can be done without damaging the picture. If this is impossible, have a copy made with a copier or by a photographic laboratory, and record the information there. It is well worth having all pictures

copied anyway. At the least, you should record your information on a sheet of paper with the fullest possible description of the picture.

Your data should include the subject of the picture and its familial relationship to you. The relevant code number or numbers should be marked. When and where it was taken should be recorded if possible, and how you acquired it. You may wish to make extra copies to fix in this album, and any family photograph album. But do keep rare photographic originals safe; perhaps in a safety deposit box. They can be very precious indeed, and are usually irreplaceable.

Using Family Sources

Now, with your notebook and miscellaneous file prepared in the coded system, you are ready to start recording what you already know. Put it in the workbook first, and then copy it into this album. When you've filled in everything you know personally, you'll find you still need more data. On page 15 is a 'Family History Questionnaire'. Copy it and mail it to all your family members, keeping a record of who has had it and when you sent it. A telephone call and accompanying letter should help get their assistance. If you don't hear from anyone within a reasonable time, follow up with another call or letter. Don't forget to send them stamped addressed envelopes!

Some people may prefer a personal interview. Some one may have a Family Bible – an invaluable source for the family historian. Someone may know of a relative who has already compiled a family history. Usually at least one person has some mementos, and may not be aware of their value. Talk to as many people as you can to trace such additional family sources.

Soon you will regret not having asked some deceased relative questions only they could answer. When you approach the living, start with the eldest and be tactful and considerate. A personal visit is advisable: many old people are not at their best on the telephone and can have difficulty in writing. Their memories may be hazy and too many questions can confuse them. It's best to write in advance explaining as simply as possible what you are doing and how they can help. Then telephone them asking when it would be convenient to visit.

Your visit will be more productive if you limit the number of questions you ask. Write down the information you want to obtain – names, dates, relationships – before you go. If your informant has no objection, it is well worth tape recording the interview, or having someone with you to take notes. Ask first! If you yourself keep stopping to write down what you hear, elderly people may lose their train of thought.

Sometimes they won't want to discuss certain family members or events – almost all families have their secrets!

Old people tire easily, so it is best to have several shorter sessions if possible. Bring along any old photographs you have for identification – they can jog the memory wonderfully! And you can interest your interviewees by telling them what you have already discovered. Do ask if they have any additional family source material as listed on page 94.

And always write a thankyou letter afterward!

The origin of your surname

The study of surnames is a full-time occupation for some genealogists. Most of you will already know the derivation of your surname. It is, however, still worth referring to *The Oxford Dictionary of Surnames* which can be found in the reference sections of most larger libraries. The further back you go in time, the more localized surname distribution is likely to be. Very few English-descended families will find their names in the Domesday Book. Surnames were fairly new in 1066, and only held by great landowners. The name usually signified the family home, though as we shall see, William the Conqueror's adversary at the Battle of Hastings used a patronymic.

By the fifteenth century surnames were

fairly well established. They could be based on residence (Washington, Lincoln, Roosevelt), occupation (Smith, Chandler, Taylor), physical appearance (Small, Round, Pauncefoot – from the old French words 'paunce forte' for Big Belly), nicknames and a variety of other identifiers.

Among the commonest in northern Europe were patronymics: names identifying the holder as 'son of' his father. Thus in the Germanic languages the suffixes -son and -sen are common. King Harold who died at the Battle of Hastings was named Harold Godwinson for his father, the famous earl Godwin. Some Scandinavian languages identified daughters with the suffixes -dotter or -datter. Gaelic Mac, Mc and M' all signify "son of", as does the welsh ap, often shortened to a single P as in Pritchard – ap Richard – or Price – ap Rhys.

Many Americans will find their original family names have been changed, simplified or shortened. It was common practice for immigration authorities to alter European names at will. Or someone in your family may have chosen to Americanize the name themselves. Danny Kaye's original surname was Kaminsky, and many other former Kaminskys are now called Kaye or Kay. You may also have to translate your name to understand its meaning.

The old home visit

It can be an incredibly exciting experience to stand on the very spot where your ancestors once lived. Planning your visit carefully helps make it even more rewarding. Most people choose to visit the original homesite of their family before all later generations have moved away. Having as much information as possible before you travel can make a huge contribution to the value of your trip. Find out who lived there, how they made their living, where they worshipped and what part they played in community life. Contact the local reference library, the Historical Society, the local government offices, schools and places of worship. They may be able to provide you with information before you start out, and should be able to tell you what records are available for you to see. Plan your trip taking due note of the days when these resources are open for you to consult.

If there are family members still living in the area be sure to inform them of your visit and make plans to meet with them. Be sure you record your visit using as many means as possible. Take notes and photographs. A video-recording will be especially treasured by present and future generations.

Those of us with immigrant parents or grandparents may wish to visit the land they came from. It is even more important to know as much as possible before planning such a trip, and proper preparation is essential. Contact the Embassy or High Commission of the country you will be visiting and enlist their help. You may need a guide or interpreter to help if you don't speak the language. Since this may be an expensive trip, don't undertake it lightly. But properly planned, this is likely to be the experience of a lifetime for those who undertake it.

Continuing your research

When you have gone as far as you can using family sources you will probably be intimidated by a mass of blank spaces on the latter pages of your family tree. Unless someone else in your family has undertaken extensive genealogical research you are likely to have found few, if any, of your great-great-grandparents, and none of your great-great-greats. These just aren't relatives any of us remember!

There are three options you can now follow. You may decide to leave the album as it is for future generations to enjoy and extend if they choose. You might alternatively decide to hire a professional researcher to complete your work. Since this can be quite expensive it is vital that whoever you employ is a good and reliable agent. Most countries have a regulating body for researchers which should guarantee the work of their members. Consult one of the genealogical societies listed on page 95 for their guidance.

It is best to read at least one introductory book on genealogical research. There are some suggestions on page 95. Many communities have a Family History or Genealogy Club where you can meet other people engaged in similar research. they can be a source of much helpful guidance. Your local library will know if such a group exists.

For those who have the dedication, tracing out your family can be a real labour of love. But whatever you choose to do, by filling entries in this book you have already accomplished something of great value for your family.

Congratulations!

our Family

This album was researched and assembled by:

Name ....

When ....

Where ....

Family History

Name .... Date ....

1. What was your date of birth? ....

2. Where were you born? ....

3. What were your parents' full names at the time of your marriage? Your grandparents' names?
    ....

4. Who are your brothers and sisters, and when and where were they born?
    ....
    ....
    ....

5. What schools did you attend? Further education? Awards or honours?
    ....
    ....

6. What is your occupation? ....

7. What are your hobbies? ....
    ....

8. What is your religious affiliation? ....

9. If married, what was the full name of your spouse at the time of your marriage?
    ....

10. When and where did you marry? ....

11. Who attended your wedding? ....
    ....

12. Who was in your bridal party? ....
    ....

13. Where was your wedding reception? ....

14. How many children do you have? What are their names? When and where were they born?
    ....
    ....

15. Did you or any of your antecedents serve in the armed forces? If so, give details. ....
    ....

16. Do you know of any family members who have traced their forebears? ....

17. Please give all the information you have concerning our family history, including birth and death ..
    dates of family members. ....
    ....

18. Give the details of any family reunions or functions you may have attended.
    ....

19. Please include any additional information that you feel is relevant
    ....

Husband

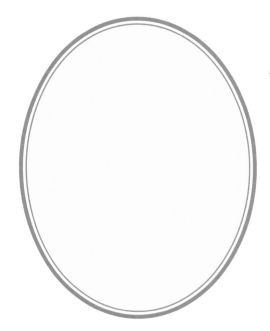

Name ....

Place of birth ....

Mother's maiden name ....

Childhood home ....

Education ....

Occupation ....

Hobbies ....

Religious affiliation ....

Wife

Maiden name ....

Place of birth ....

Mother's maiden name ....

Childhood home ....

Education ....

Occupation ....

Hobbies ....

Religious affiliation ....

Reader,
I married him.

CHARLOTTE
BRONTE

17

our Wedding

Date ....

Place ....

Type of ceremony ....

Officiating minister or registrar ....

Best Man ....

Your brother and sister no sooner met, but they looked; no sooner looked but they loved; no sooner loved but they sighed; no sooner sighed but they asked one another the reason; no sooner knew the reason but they sought the remedy; and in these degrees have they made a pair of stairs to marriage.

SHAKESPEARE

Maid of Honor ....

Bridesmaids and pages ....

Organist or musicians ....

The Reception ....

Place ....

Lasted from .... to ....

Catered by ....

Who served ....

Speeches by ....

Music by ....

*The bride hath
paced into the hall,
Red as a rose is she;
Nodding their heads
before her goes
The merry
minstrelsy.*

C O L E R I D G E

our Honeymoon

Where we went ....

From .... to ....

How we travelled ....

Where we stayed ....

What we did ....

....

....

Places we visited ....

....

What we enjoyed most ....

....

Come aboard for all the fun of France

Once aboard a great French Line ship to Europe, you are forever spoiled for any voyage less enchanting.

You find the very air sparkles with the fun-loving spirit of France. You relax to the French flair for elegance gracious service. Your appetite revels in th French cuisine, recognized the world's f with interesting new friends, to merr

Almost with regret you a ready for the sights and f

REGULAR SAILINGS FROM NEW YORK:
The magnificent 51,840-ton **Liberté**, Sept. 1*, 18.
The gracious, storied **Ile de France**, Aug. 24, Sept. 11.
The intimate **Flandre**, Sept. 5, 24.
*On Sept. 1 the Liberté sails at 12:05 A.M.

our First home

We lived there from .... to ....

Address ....

Description ....

Improvements we made ....

Our neighbours were ....

later Moves

Address ....

....

From .... to ....

Address ....

....

From .... to ....

Address ....

....

From .... to ....

our Professional life

Husband

EDUCATION

Schools attended and dates ....
....
....
....

Further education and dates ....
....

OCCUPATION

First job ....
Dates ....
Job description ....

Job ....
Dates ....
Job description ....

Job ....
Dates ....
Job description ....

WIFE

EDUCATION

Schools attended with dates

....

....

....

....

Further education with dates ....

....

OCCUPATION

First job ....

Dates ....

Job description ....

Job ....

Dates ....

Job description ....

Job ....

Dates ....

Job description ....

*Women's
work is never done.*

PROVERBIAL

our Children

Name ....

Place of birth ....

Education ....

Hobbies ....

Occupation ....

Married to ....

Date of marriage ....

God bless the master of this house, Likewise the mistress too, And all the little children That round the table go: Love and joy come to you...

WASSAILING SONG

Name ....

Place of birth ....

Education ....

Hobbies ....

Occupation ....

Married to ....

Date of marriage ....

*Happy is the man
that has his quiver
full of children.*

PSALM 127

Name ....

Place of birth ....

Education ....

Hobbies ....

Occupation ....

Married to ....

Date of marriage ....

our Children

Name ....

Place of birth ....

Education ....

Hobbies ....

Occupation ....

Married to ....

Date of marriage ....

*Thou art thy
mother's glass,
and she in thee
Calls back the
lovely April of
her prime.*

SHAKESPEARE

Name ....

Place of birth ....

Education ....

Hobbies ....

Occupation ....

Married to ....

Date of marriage ....

Baby boy,
recognize your
mother with a smile.
VIRGIL

Name ....

Place of birth ....

Education ....

Hobbies ....

Occupation ....

Married to ....

Date of marriage ....

*Y*our Grandchildren

Name ....

Father ....

Mother ....

Birthdate ....

She might ha
been a grandam
ere she died;
And so may you,
for a light heart
lives long.

SHAKESPEARE

Name ....

Father ....

Mother ....

Birthdate ....

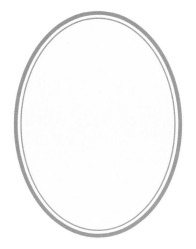

Name ....

Father ....

Mother ....

Birthdate ....

*Wisdom is
justified of her
children.*

MATTHEW, 11:19

Name ....

Father ....

Mother ....

Birthdate ....

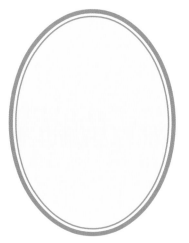

Name ....

Father ....

Mother ....

Birthdate ....

our Grandchildren

*... see the children
sport upon the shore,
And hear the
mighty waters rolling
evermore.*

WORDSWORTH

Name ....

Father ....

Mother ....

Birthdate ....

32

Name ....

Father ....

Mother ....

Birthdate ....

Name ....

Father ....

Mother ....

Birthdate ....

Name ....

Father ....

Mother ....

Birthdate ....

husband's Brothers

Name ....

Address ....

....

Wedding date ....

Birthdate ....

Wedding place ....

Place of birth ....

Children's names ....

Education ....

....

Occupation ....

Hobbies ....

Religious affiliation ....

Name ....

Spouse's name ....

Address ....

....

*I've wandered
east, I've
wandered west
Through mony a
weary way;
But never, never
can forget
The love o' life's
young day.*

WILLIAM
MOTHERWELL

Birthdate ....

Place of birth ....

Education ....

Occupation ....

Hobbies ....

Religious affiliation ....

Spouse's name ....

Wedding date ....

Wedding place ....

Children's names ....

....

34

and Sisters

Name ....
Address ....
....

Birthdate ....
Place of birth ....
Education ....
Occupation ....
Hobbies ....
Religious affiliation ....
Spouse's name ....
Wedding date ....
Wedding place ....
Children's names ....
....

Name ....
Address ....
....

Birthdate ....

Place of birth ....
Education ....
Occupation ....
Hobbies ....
Religious affiliation ....
Spouse's name ....
Wedding date ....
Wedding place ....
Children's names ....
....

...there is no friend like a sister In calm or stormy weather.

CHRISTINA
ROSSETTI

wife's Brothers

Name ....

Address ....

....

Birthdate ....

Place of birth ....

Education ....

Occupation ....

Hobbies ....

Religious affiliation ....

Spouse's name ....

Wedding date ....

Wedding place ....

Children's names ....

....

Name ....

Address ....

....

Birthdate ....

Place of birth ....

Education ....

....

Occupation ....

Hobbies ....

Religious affiliation ....

....

Spouse's name ....

Wedding date ....

Wedding place ....

Children's names ....

....

....

and *Sisters*

The roaring of the wind is my wife and the stars through the window pane are my children.

JOHN KEATS

Name

Address

Birthdate

Place of birth

Education

Occupation

Hobbies

Religious affiliation

Spouse's name

Wedding date

Wedding place

Children's names

Name

Address

Birthdate

Place of birth

Education

Occupation

Hobbies

Religious affiliation

Spouse's name

Wedding date

Wedding place

Children's names

husband's Father

Name ....

Address ....

....

Birthdate ....

Birthplace ....

Education ....

Military service ....

Occupation ....

Hobbies ....

Religious affiliation ....

Wedding date and place ....

Mother's name ....

Father's name ....

When all the world is old, lad, And all the trees are brown.... God grant you find one face there, You loved when all was young.

CHARLES
KINGSLEY

I grow old ever learning many things.

SOLON

husband's Mother

Name

Address

Birthdate

Birthplace

Education

Occupation

Hobbies

Religious affiliation

Wedding date and place

Mother's name

Father's name

*In the dark room
where I began
My mother's life
made me a man
Through all the
months of
human birth
Her beauty fed my
common earth.*

JOHN MASEFIELD

wife's Father

*Tho' much is
taken, much abides;
and tho'
We are not now
that strength which
in old days
Moved earth and
heaven; that which
we are, we are;
One equal temper
of heroic hearts
Made weak by
time and fate,
but strong in will,*

TENNYSON

Name ....

Address ....

....

Birthdate ....

Birthplace ....

Education ....

Military service ....

Occupation ....

Hobbies ....

Religious affiliation ....

Wedding date and place ....

Mother's name ....

Father's name ....

wife's Mother

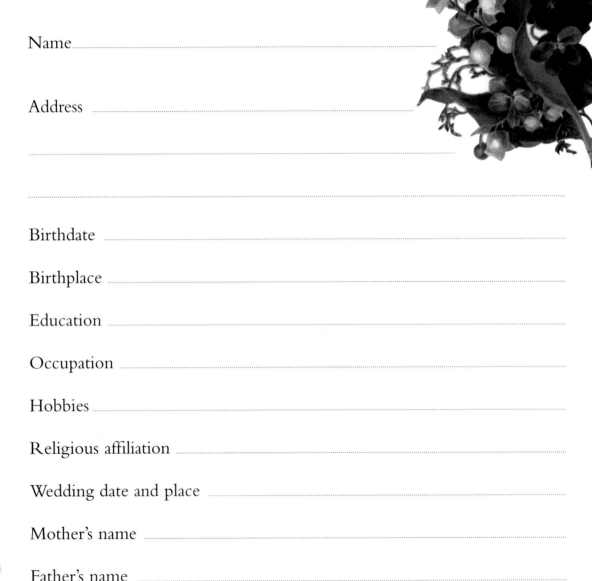

Name ....

Address ....

....

....

Birthdate ....

Birthplace ....

Education ....

Occupation ....

Hobbies ....

Religious affiliation ....

Wedding date and place ....

Mother's name ....

Father's name ....

They sin who tell
us love can die.
With life all other
passions fly,
All others are but
vanity.

ROBERT SOUTHEY

husband's Aunts

Name ....

Address ....

....

Birthdate ....

Place of birth ....

Education ....

Occupation ....

Hobbies ....

Religious affiliation ....

Spouse's name ....

Wedding date ....

Wedding Place ....

Children's names ....

....

....

Name ....

Address ....

....

Birthdate ....

Place of birth ....

Education ....

Occupation ....

Hobbies ....

Religious affiliation ....

Spouse's name ....

Wedding date ....

Wedding place ....

Children's names ....

....

....

Name ....

Address ....

....

Birthdate ....

Place of birth ....

Education ....

Occupation ....

Hobbies ....

Religious affiliation ....

Spouse's name ....

Wedding date ....

Wedding place ....

Children's names ....

....

and $\mathcal{U}$ncles

Name ....

Address ....

....

Birthdate ....

Place of birth ....

Education ....

Occupation ....

Hobbies ....

Religious affiliation ....

Spouse's name ....

Wedding date ....

Wedding place ....

Children's names ....

....

❦

Name ....

Address ....

....

Birthdate ....

Place of birth ....

Education ....

Occupation ....

Hobbies ....

Religious affiliation ....

Spouse's name ....

Wedding date ....

Wedding place ....

Children's names ....

....

....

❦

Name ....

Address ....

....

Birthdate ....

Place of birth ....

Education ....

Occupation ....

Hobbies ....

Religious affiliation ....

Spouse's name ....

Wedding date ....

Wedding place ....

Children's names ....

....

....

....

wife's Aunts

Name ....

Address ....

....

Birthdate ....

Place of birth ....

Education ....

Occupation ....

Hobbies ....

Religious affiliation ....

Spouse's name ....

Wedding date ....

Wedding place ....

Children's names ....

....

....

❧❧❧

Name ....

Address ....

....

Birthdate ....

Place of birth ....

Education ....

Occupation ....

Hobbies ....

Religious affiliation ....

Spouse's name ....

Wedding date ....

Wedding place ....

Children's names ....

❧❧❧

Name ....

Address ....

....

Birthdate ....

Place of birth ....

Education ....

Occupation ....

Hobbies ....

Religious affiliation ....

Spouse's name ....

Wedding date ....

Wedding place ....

Children's names ....

....

and *Uncles*

Name ....

Address ....

....

Birthdate ....

Place of birth ....

Education ....

Occupation ....

Hobbies ....

Religious affiliation ....

Spouse's name ....

Wedding date ....

Wedding place ....

Children's names ....

....

Name ....

Address ....

....

Birthdate ....

Place of birth ....

Education ....

Occupation ....

Hobbies ....

Religious affiliation ....

Spouse's name ....

Wedding date ....

Wedding place ....

Children's names ....

....

Name ....

Address ....

....

Birthdate ....

Place of birth ....

Education ....

Occupation ....

Hobbies ....

Religious affiliation ....

Spouse's name ....

Wedding date ....

Wedding place ....

Children's names ....

Nice old geezer with a nasty cough, Sees my Missus, takes 'is topper off In a very gentlemanly way! 'Ma'am,' says he, ' I 'ave some news to tell, Your rich Uncle Tom of Camberwell Popped off recent, which it ain't a sell, Leaving you 'is little Donkey Shay.'
"Knocked 'em in the Old Kent Road"

MUSIC HALL SONG

49

husband's Cousins

Name ....

Address ....

....

Birthdate ....

Place of birth ....

Education ....

Occupation ....

Hobbies ....

Religious affiliation ....

Spouse's name ....

Wedding date ....

Wedding place ....

Children's names ....

....

Name ....

Address ....

....

Birthdate ....

Place of birth ....

Education ....

Occupation ....

Hobbies ....

Religious affiliation ....

Spouse's name ....

Wedding date ....

Wedding place ....

Children's names ....

Name ....

Address ....

....

Birthdate ....

Place of birth ....

Education ....

Occupation ....

Hobbies ....

Religious affiliation ....

Spouse's name ....

Wedding date ....

Wedding place ....

Children's names ....

....

Name ....

Address ....

....

Birthdate ....

Place of birth ....

Education ....

Occupation ....

Hobbies ....

Religious affiliation ....

Spouse's name ....

Wedding date ....

Wedding place ....

Children's names ....

....

....

Name ....

Address ....

....

Birthdate ....

Place of birth ....

Education ....

Occupation ....

Hobbies ....

Religious affiliation ....

....

Spouse's name ....

Wedding date ....

Wedding place ....

Children's names ....

....

....

Name ....

Address ....

....

Birthdate ....

Place of birth ....

Education ....

Occupation ....

Hobbies ....

Religious affiliation ....

Spouse's name ....

Wedding date ....

Wedding place ....

Children's names ....

..close affection grows from common names, from kindred blood...

EDMUND BURKE

51

wife's Cousins

Name ....

Address ....

....

Birthdate ....

Place of birth ....

Education ....

Occupation ....

Hobbies ....

Religious affiliation ....

Spouse's name ....

Wedding date ....

Wedding place ....

Children's names ....

....

Wedding date ....

Wedding place ....

Children's names ....

....

O coz, coz, coz,
my pretty little coz,
that thou didst know
how many fathoms
deep I am in love!

SHAKESPEARE

Name ....

Address ....

....

Birthdate ....

Place of birth ....

Education ....

Occupation ....

Hobbies ....

Religious affiliation ....

Spouse's name ....

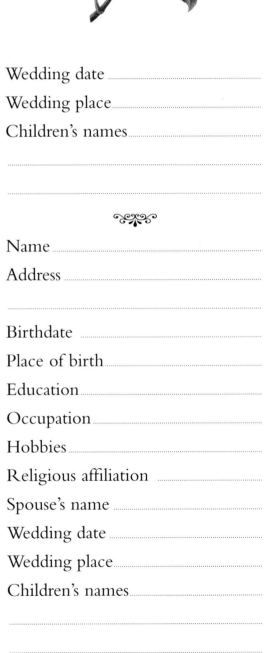

Name ....

Address ....

....

Birthdate ....

Place of birth ....

Education ....

Occupation ....

Hobbies ....

Religious affiliation ....

Spouse's name ....

Wedding date ....

Wedding place ....

Children's names ....

....

Name ....
Address ....

....

Birthdate ....
Place of birth ....
Education ....
Occupation ....
Hobbies ....
Religious affiliation ....
Spouse's name ....
Wedding date ....
Wedding place ....
Children's names ....

....

Name ....
Address ....

....

Birthdate ....
Place of birth ....
Education ....
Occupation ....
Hobbies ....
Religious affiliation ....
Spouse's name ....
Wedding date ....
Wedding place ....
Children's names ....

....

Name ....
Address ....

....

Birthdate ....
Place of birth ....
Education ....
Occupation ....
Hobbies ....
Religious affiliation ....
Spouse's name ....
Wedding date ....
Wedding place ....
Children's names ....

....

"Every day when he looked into the glass, and gave the last touch to his consummate toilette, he offered his grateful thanks to Providence that his family was not unworthy of him.

DISRAELI

GRANDFATHER   GRANDMOTHER

Name    Name

From .... to ....   From .... to ....

Birthplace ....   Birthplace ....

Occupation ....   Occupation ....

Wedding date and place

....

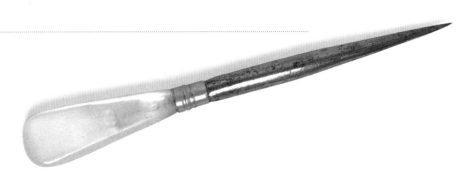

One of the last
dances was an
old-fashioned
country dance called
'the grandfather',
when each couple
in turn passed
along holding a
handkerchief,
over which
all the others had
to jump.

PALL MALL
MAGAZINE 1897

The markes
which were in the
body of the
Grandfather do
often appeare in the
Grandchilde.

HELKIAH CROOKE

GRANDFATHER

GRANDMOTHER

Name..

From......................... to ....

Birthplace ....

Occupation ....

Name..

From......................... to ....

Birthplace ....

Occupation ....

Wedding date and place

wifes's Grandparents

GRANDFATHER

GRANDMOTHER

Name ....

From .... to ....

Birthplace ....

Occupation ....

Name ....

From .... to ....

Birthplace ....

Occupation ....

Wedding date and place

....

GRANDFATHER

GRANDMOTHER

Name..

From.................... to ....

Birthplace ....

Occupation ....

Name..

From.................... to ....

Birthplace ....

Occupation ....

Wedding date and place

*Y*our Immediate family

*There's nothing
wrong in a
connubial kiss*

B Y R O N

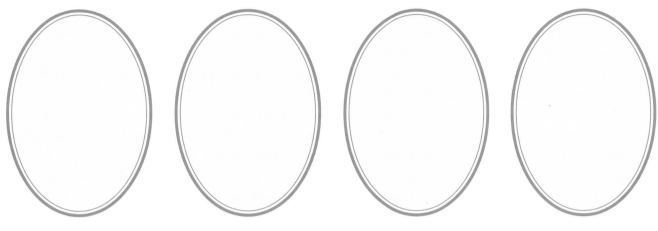

WIFE'S PARENTS   HUSBAND'S PARENTS

WIFE   HUSBAND

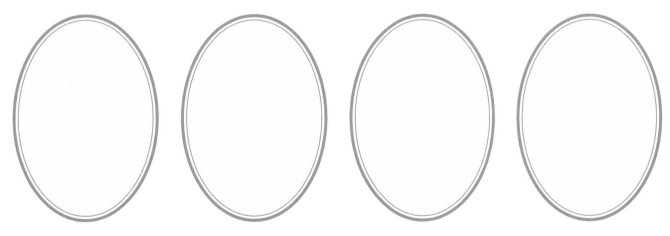

CHILDREN

our Family tree

Husband ....

Wife ....

Date of marriage ....

Place of marriage ....

Children ....

....

....

....

Husband's Father ....

Husband's Mother ....

Date of marriage ....

Place of marriage ....

Children ....

....

Wife's Father ....

Wife's Mother ....

Date of marriage ....

Place of marriage ....

Children ....

....

....

Husband's paternal Grandfather ....

Husband's paternal Grandmother ....

Date and place of marriage ....

Children ....

....

....

Husband's maternal Grandfather ....

Husband's maternal Grandmother ....

Date and place of marriage ....

Children ....

....

....

Wife's paternal Grandfather ....

Wife's paternal Grandmother ....

Date and place of marriage ....

Children ....

....

....

Wife's maternal Grandfather ....

Wife's maternal Grandmother ....

Date and place of marriage ....

Children ....

....

....

Husband's Great-Grandfather

Husband's Great-Grandmother

Husband's Great-Grandfather

Husband's Great-Grandmother

Husband's Great-Grandfather

Husband's Great-Grandmother

Husband's Great-Grandfather

Husband's Great-Grandmother

Husband's Great-
Great-Grandfather

Husband's Great-Great
-Grandmother

Husband's Great-Great-Grandfather

Husband's Great-Great-Grandmother

Husband's Great-Great-Grandfather

Husband's Great-Great Grandmother

Husband's Great-Great-Grandfather

Husband's Great-Great-Grandmother

Husband's Great-Great-Grandfather

Husband's Great-Great-Grandmother

Husband's Great-Great-Grandfather

Husband's Great-Great-Grandmother

Husband's Great-Great-Grandfather

Husband's Great-Great-Grandmother

Husband's Great-Great-Grandfather

Husband's Great-Great-Grandmother

Wife's Great-Great-Grandfather

Wife's Great-Great-Grandmother

Wife's Great-Grandfather

Wife's Great-Great-Grandfather

Wife's Great-Grandmother

Wife's Great-Great-Grandmother

Wife's Great-Grandfather

Wife's Great-Great-Grandfather

Wife's Great-Grandmother

Wife's Great-Great-Grandmother

Wife's Great-Great-Grandfather

Wife's Great-Great-Grandmother

Wife's Great-Grandfather

Wife's Great-Great-Grandfather

Wife's Great-Grandmother

Wife's Great-Great-Grandmother

Wife's Great-Grandfather

Wife's Great-Great-Grandfather

Wife's Great-Grandmother

Wife's Great-Great-Grandmother

Wife's Great-Great-Grandfather

Wife's Great-Great-Grandmother

Our great-great-great-

Mr and Mrs .... Née ....

Mr and Mrs .... Née ....

Mr and Mrs .... Née ....

Mr and Mrs .... Née ....

Mr and Mrs .... Née ....

Mr and Mrs .... Née ....

Mr and Mrs .... Née ....

Mr and Mrs .... Née ....

Mr and Mrs .... Née ....

Mr and Mrs .... Née ....

Mr and Mrs .... Née ....

Mr and Mrs .... Née ....

Mr and Mrs .... Née ....

Mr and Mrs .... Née ....

Mr and Mrs .... Née ....

Mr and Mrs .... Née ....

Mr and Mrs .... Née ....

Mr and Mrs .... Née ....

Mr and Mrs .... Née ....

$\mathcal{G}$randparents

Mr and Mrs	Née
Mr and Mrs	Née
Mr and Mrs	Née
Mr and Mrs	Née
Mr and Mrs	Née
Mr and Mrs	Née
Mr and Mrs	Née
Mr and Mrs	Née
Mr and Mrs	Née
Mr and Mrs	Née
Mr and Mrs	Née
Mr and Mrs	Née
Mr and Mrs	Née

Our great–great-great–

Mr and Mrs .... Née ....

Mr and Mrs .... Née ....

Mr and Mrs .... Née ....

Mr and Mrs .... Née ....

Mr and Mrs .... Née ....

Mr and Mrs .... Née ....

Mr and Mrs .... Née ....

Mr and Mrs .... Née ....

Mr and Mrs .... Née ....

Mr and Mrs .... Née ....

Mr and Mrs .... Née ....

Mr and Mrs .... Née ....

Mr and Mrs .... Née ....

Mr and Mrs .... Née ....

Mr and Mrs .... Née ....

Mr and Mrs .... Née ....

Mr and Mrs .... Née ....

Mr and Mrs .... Née ....

Mr and Mrs .... Née ....

Grandparents

Mr and Mrs .... Née ....

Mr and Mrs .... Née ....

Mr and Mrs .... Née ....

Mr and Mrs .... Née ....

Mr and Mrs .... Née ....

Mr and Mrs .... Née ....

Mr and Mrs .... Née ....

Mr and Mrs .... Née ....

Mr and Mrs .... Née ....

Mr and Mrs .... Née ....

Mr and Mrs .... Née ....

Mr and Mrs .... Née ....

Mr and Mrs .... Née ....

our Ancestors

Name

Place of origin

Additional information

Name

Place of origin

Additional information

Name

Place of origin

Additional information

Name

Place of origin

Additional information

*Afoot and
light-hearted
I take to the
open road,
Healthy, free,
the world
before me.*

WALT WHITMAN

Name ....

Place of origin ....

Additional information ....

....

....

Name ....

Place of origin ....

Additional information ....

....

....

...tired with the labour of far travel we have come to our own home and rest on the couch we have longed for.

CATULLUS

Name ....

Place of origin ....

Additional information ....

....

....

Name ....

Place of origin ....

Additional information ....

....

....

our $\mathcal{F}$amily name

What does our surname mean?

....

....

....

....

....

From what language does it originate?

....

....

....

....

....

Has it been Anglicized from an original version, or changed in any other way from an older form?

Is it spelled in any other ways?

Are there any famous people bearing our surname?

our First names

Name ....

What does this name mean? ....

Additional information ....

....

....

....

Name ....

What does this name mean? ....

Additional information ....

....

....

....

Name ....

What does this name mean? ....

Additional information ....

....

....

....

Name ....

What does this name mean? ....

Additional information ....

....

....

....

Name ....

What does this name mean? ....

Additional information ....

....

....

....

Name ....

What does this name mean? ....

Additional information ....

....

....

....

family Weddings

Bride ....
Groom ....
Place and date ....
Bride's parents ....
Attendants ....
Place of reception ....
Guests ....

....

Bride ....
Groom ....
Place and date ....
Bride's parents ....
Attendants ....
Place of reception ....
Guests ....

....

Bride ....
Groom ....
Place and date ....
Bride's parents ....
Attendants ....
Place of reception ....
Guests ....

....

Bride ....

Groom ....

Place and date ....

Bride's parents ....

Attendants ....

Place of reception ....

Guests ....

....

....

Bride ....

Groom ....

Place and date ....

Bride's parents ....

Attendants ....

Place of reception ....

Guests ....

....

....

family Reunions

When was it held ....
Where ....
Were there special activities? ....
....
Who attended? ....
....
....
....

When was it held ....
Where ....
Were there special activities? ....
....
Who attended? ....
....
....
....

When was it held ....
Where ....
Were there special activities? ....
....
Who attended? ....
....
....
....

When was it held ....
Where ....
Were there special activities? ....
....
Who attended? ....
....
....
....
....

When was it held ....
Where ....
Were there special activities? ....
....
Who attended? ....
....
....
....
....

*Is it a party
in a parlour?
Cramm'd just as
they on earth
were cramm'd -
Some sipping punch,
some sipping tea,*

WORDSWORTH

family Reunions

When was it held ....
Where ....
Were there special activities? ....
....
Who attended? ....
....
....
....
....

When was it held ....
Where ....
Were there special activities? ....
....
Who attended? ....
....
....
....
....

When was it held ....
Where ....
Were there special activities? ....
....
Who attended? ....
....
....
....
....

When was it held ....
Where ....
Were there special activities? ....
....
Who attended? ....
....
....
....
....

When was it held ....
Where ....
Were there special activities? ....
....
Who attended? ....
....
....
....
....

family Holidays

Date ....

Place ....

....

....

Date ....

Place ....

....

....

Date ....

Place ....

....

....

family Vacations

Where we went ....

When .... to ....

How we travelled ....

Where we stayed ....

What we did ....

....

Where we went ....

When .... to ....

How we travelled ....

Where we stayed ....

What we did ....

....

Where we went ....

When .... to ....

How we travelled ....

Where we stayed ....

What we did ....

....

....

Where we went ....

When .... to ....

How we travelled..

Where we stayed ....

What we did ....

....

important Times

What historical events in your lifetime have affected you most?

Tho' lost to sight,
to mem'ry dear
Thou ever wilt
remain.

GEORGE LINLEY

in our lives

Have either of you ever met any famous people?

important Times

What has been the most exciting time you can remember?

What have been your happiest times, and why?

the Old home visit

What town or city did you visit? ....

Who lived there? ....

When .... to ....

Address ....

What town or city did you visit? ....

Who lived there? ....

When .... to ....

Address ....

What town or city did you visit? ....

Who lived there? ....

When .... to ....

Address ....

What town or city did you visit? ....

Who lived there? ....

When .... to ....

Address ....

*Such is
the patriot's boast,
where'er we roam,
His first,
best country ever
is at home.*

OLIVER GOLDSMITH

Do any family members still live in these places?

If the family has all moved away, why?

Are any of your old family homes still standing?

*We look
before and after,
And pine for
what is not:
Our sincerest
laughter
With some pain
is fraught.*

SHELLEY

What were these places like when your family lived there? Have they changed much? What part did the family play in the life of these communities? How did they earn their living?

the Old home visit

What was the family's place of worship? ....
....

Are family members buried there? ....
How many? ....

Who .... Who ....

From .... From ....
To .... To ....

Who .... Who ....

From .... From ....
To .... To ....

Who .... Who ....

From .... From ....
To .... To ....

What other information did you learn from the records?
(Marriages, baptisms, confirmations etc.) ....
....
....
....

*To marry is
to domesticate the
Recording Angel.*

R.L.STEVENSON

a *R*ecord of your visits

Photographs

Homes ....

....

Land ....

Home site. ....

Area ....

Places of worship ....

Cemetery ....

Family business ....

Family members still there ....

....

Video contents ....

....

....

Tape recordings contents ....

....

Copies ....

Maps ....

Religious records ....

Civic records ....

Additional information:

....

....

....

Special memories

Name ....

Family relationship ....

From .... to ....

Place of burial ....

Name ....

Family relationship ....

From .... to ....

Place of burial ....

Name ....

Family relationship ....

From .... to ....

Place of burial ....

Name ....

Family relationship ....

From .... to ....

Place of burial ....

*Beneath those
rugged elms,
that yew-tree's shade,
Where heaves the
turf in many a
mouldering heap,
Each in his narrow
cell forever laid,
The rude forefathers
of the hamlet sleep.*

THOMAS GRAY

92

Name ....

Family relationship ....

From .... to ....

Place of burial ....

Name ....

Family relationship ....

From .... to ....

Place of burial ....

Name ....

Family relationship ....

From .... to ....

Place of burial ....

Name ....

Family relationship ....

From .... to ....

Place of burial ....

The glories of
our blood and state
Are shadows, not
substantial things;
There is no armour
against fate;
Death lays his icy
hand on kings:
Sceptre and crown
Must tumble down,
And in the dust be
equal made
With the poor
crooked scythe and
spade.

JAMES SHIRLEY

useful Names and addresses

Additional Family Sources

Address Books and lists
Albums, Photographs etc.
Autograph Books
Awards
Baby Books
Baptismal or Christening Records
Bar Mitzvah or Bas Mitzvah records
Bible entries
Biographical notes
Birth Announcements
Birth Certificates
Birthday Books
Books (clippings, inscriptions, etc.)
Business records
Certificates
Church Membership records
Citizenship Papers
Club and Society Records
Confirmation Records
Congratulatory Messages
Death Certificates and Burial Records
Deeds
Diaries
Diplomas
Education and School Records: Reports, Awards, Certificates, Registers
Employment Records
Engagement Announcements
Family Associations
Family Trees and Charts
Funeral Memorial Cards
Genealogies (unpublished)
House/Land purchases or sales
Insurance Records Leases and rents
Legal Papers and Solicitors' Letters
Ledgers
Letters
Licenses

Life Sketches (unpublished)
Maps
Marriage Certificates, Contracts, Licences and Settlements
Membership Certificates: Boy Scouts, Lodges, Political Parties, etc
Mementoes
Memorials
Military Records: Citations, Conscription Burial or Cemetery Record, Discharge, Orders, Pensions, Veterans' Benefits, etc.
Mortgages
Naturalization Papers
Newspapers and Clippings
Notebooks
Obituaries
Oral family History and Traditions
Passports and Applications
Photographs and names on front and back of the same
Pictures
Portraits and Paintings
Professional Certificates (Teaching, Pharmacy etc.)
Promotion Notices
Receipts
Retirement/Superannuation Records
Souvenirs
Surveys of Property
Tax Bills, Receipts and Returns
Telegrams
Telephone Number Lists
Tombstone Inscriptions
University and College Records: Degree and Graduation Certificates and Lists
Wills and Probate Documents
Yearbooks (School, University, Church etc.)

Useful Addresses

The Family History Department
Genealogical Library
Church of the Latter Day Saints
35 N.W. Temple Street
Salt Lake City
Utah 84150

National Genealogical Society
4527 17th Street North
Arlington
Virginia 22207-2363

National Archives and Records
Service NNC
Washington DC 20408

American Society of Genealogists
1228 Eye Street NW
Washington DC 20005

Ontario Genealogical Society
Box 74
Station U
Toronto Ontario M82 5M4

The Genealogical Publishing Co. Inc.
111 Water Street
Angus Baxter,
Maryland 21201

New York Genealogical and Biographical
Society
122 East 58th Street
New York
NY 10022

New England Historic Genealogical Society
101 Newbury Street
Boston
Massachusetts 02116

Family History Association of Canada
P.O.Box 398
West Vancouver
British Columbia V7V 3P10

Recommended Books

Timothy Field Beard,
How to Find Your Family Roots,
McGraw-Hill, 1977

★ Elizabeth Petty Bentley,
The Genealogist's Address Book,
Genealogical Publishing Co., 1991

G.H.Doane,
Searching for your Ancestors,
Bantam Books, 1973

American Genealogical Research
Institute Staff,
How to Trace your Family Tree,
Doubleday, 1973

L.G.Pine,
*American Origins: A Handbook
of Genealogical Sources Throughout
Europe.*
Doubleday, 1960

Hugh T.Law,
How to Trace your Ancestors in Europe,
Cottonwood Books, 1987

Angus Baxter,
How to Trace your European Roots,
Genealogical Publishing Co. Inc., 1985

Tracing Your Ancestors in Canada,
Public Archives of Canada, 1972

★ Contains addresses for all state and
federal records

Credits

SELECT BIBLIOGRAPHY

Sir William Addison, *Understanding English Surnames*, Batsford, 1978

American Genealogical Research Institute Staff, *How to Trace Your Family Tree*, Doubleday, 1973

Timothy Field Beard, *How to Find Your Family Roots*, McGraw-Hill, 1977

G.H.Doane, *Searching for Your Ancestors*, Bantam Books, 1973

Patrick Hanks & Frances Hodges, *The Dictionary of Surnames*, Oxford University Press, 1989

N.T.Hansen, *Guide to Genealogical Sources – Australia and New Zealand*, 1963

M.Rubincam, *Genealogical Research Methods and Sources*, Genealogical Publications, 1966

Meg Wheeler, *Tracing your Roots*, Tiger International plc, 1996

ACKNOWLEDGEMENTS

The authors would like to thank Jeremy Palmer, B.A. and Richard Baxter Ph D., D.I.C., F.H.G. of the Institute of Heraldic and Genealogical Studies and the staff of the Guildhall Library, London.

In addition our agent, Richard Jeffs of Roger Hancock Ltd, and our editor, Sarah Larter of Carlton Books have been their usual fund of help and encouragement, and Paul Savory, as ever, has helped in more ways than we can count.

The publishers would like to thank the following sources for their kind permission to reproduce the pictures in this book:

CORBIS: /Tony Arruza 22b /Bettmann 23, 32, 45, 84 /©Werner Forman 68, 69 /Philip Gould 43, 55t/Hulton Deutsch Collection 18, 28, 37, 77 /Library of Congress 57t, 85 /Richard T. Nowitz 91/Oscar White 75; DOVER PUBLICATIONS: 2t, 4, 5tr, 6, 9tr, 10, 13, 19t, 20t, 29cr, 35bl, 40, 44, 52, 54, 56, 59, 64, 66tl, 74, 76, 88, 89, 90, 95; MARY EVANS PICTURE LIBRARY: 3, 21t, 25, 26, 34b, 35, 41, 58, 80, 83, 86; HULTON-GETTY: 39; ROBERT OPIE COLLECTION: 36.